THE GIRL
WHO
THOUGHT
SHE WAS
GOD

Aurora of the Philosophers

THE GIRL WHO THOUGHT SHE WAS GOD

ALANA EISENBARTH

THE GIRL WHO THOUGHT SHE WAS GOD

Light Realm Books
Copyright © 2019 Alana Eisenbarth

Text set in FF Milo
Printed in the United States of America.

ISBN-13: 978-0-9914649-2-0

IN THE BEGINNING WAS THE WORD,
AND THE WORD WAS WITH GOD,
AND THE WORD WAS GOD.

JOHN 1:1

WHERE THE WAY IS THE HARDEST,
GO. AND WHAT THE WORLD
DISCARDS ACCEPT AS YOUR OWN.

JAKOB BÖHME

PROLOGUE

I am trying not to ask about darkness, trying not to ask about punishment and rage. I have bred these things in the body. Now I will breed other things. So it begins in a northern land in the dead of winter, a land knowing darkness in a year incorrigibly temperate and gray, season following season as if from within a jar packed with sod, watered and shook, in which what grows is shaken again, interred and stunted. The sky slightly paler than the saturated ground, midday beneath the murky waterline. It is hailing, and I can almost pretend it snow that slops heavily down, can almost smell winter's wet woollen clasp in the din on the apartment's glass sky and the white perforations, the white ellipses ticking down faster than thought can complete itself.

Tomorrow I will show you why it is that I am here. Tomorrow, that I push further and further away in fear and mistrust. Wait, I say. And then I remember and begin again not in reaction, but intention, for it is this that I meant to show you...

conscience. First, taste.
aurora. What is it? What are you dusting across the earth?
conscience. Starch to dry the rain.

I shake the jar, and we are dry and silky. Shhh.

aurora. What is that?
conscience. Creation.

A powdery snow softens the appearance of the city until we can get out and be free.

It doesn't bother me to stay, the daemon says. Everything is here that you could want.
aurora. That you could want. But you forget me. The homogenized weather. I can't exist like this. It is flushing me out in distraction, pushing me into the same.

And so the daemon rides the train of my dress, the papery white of winter snow, we the first to mark it, he in tow, as we move out of the city onto a hill overlooking the sea.

Ω

conscience. When you were born there were others who grew off of you like leaves.
aurora. And now?
conscience. As we speak there are those who are coming. Ask to be awake when they arrive.

Ω

When I return to the hill my fingertips are stung numb with cold, corpse-white when I look down, a line drawn above the knuckles where the blood is shut off. Raynaud's phenomenon. I swing my arms until the blood flushes back into the extremities. There is pain, a strange tingle of death in the hand that glows now bright as I cast my gaze toward the sea and the flotsam of swans like broken ice adrift in a rising water table. I can't help but think of claims to lands that should not be; how we abort and turn away; how I am one of the dying animals; how what I have retracted from the world has furled within, protected, and how the blood clings and centers and will not travel far from core, the linear wall across the digits of hands and feet.

You don't need to hold so tightly anymore, I tell the one within. But this is a process.

conscience. Tell me again what it was to hear the dogs cry into tin, rain fall against the chain-link fence.

aurora. I am trying not to ask about darkness.

conscience. But you know how to strike beauty so that friction warms. Sidle up beside him, against his twitching back.

aurora. Why do you want this to break me?

conscience. Because it is still raw in you; you haven't finished yet.

aurora. If I relive those memories, I only bring more of the same. Leave it. It is done.

conscience. But if you were to release it.

aurora. Please, leave it. It is dark enough here without that. Don't you see that is why the snow?

conscience. You confined her in winter. It's part of the tale.

aurora. I heard the dogs and forced them to sleep, so that I could sleep. Is that where I should begin? I forgive myself.

conscience. But these are things that help others live.

aurora. Shall I tell you how it was then to walk the reservoir in shadow? Shall I tell you how it is that my mind functions more slowly now for having been there? How I am not the same?

conscience. Only because you cannot help it. Now show me for god's sake, so that I don't have to go through this again.

When we were children, Obadiah came with drifts so high they crested over our swing set. As we swung, a wall of snow came down in avalanche, leaving brilliant chips of light to glint over us—three beautiful daughters. Every one in four will be raped. But we were only three.

We built igloos. I will remember this years later, the sun drawing amber over the panes, how solitude might resonate more deeply in such a memory, my sister's laughter, her oval face and thickly plaited hair, a girl and her peanut-butter-colored dog traipsing across the lawn toward the little one bundled in her pale blue snowsuit, hair ablaze in the setting sun. How the light came warm through the wet dark trees and cast itself persimmon on the ground. And how in the absence of all these things barn board might gray, old paint haphazardly rolled might reflect the marred, sand and debris scuffed into every step, ground into the knees and palms and skinning the hip when one fell in her panties from the staircase unrailed. Waking later to vomit, then washing, cold in my skin, the warm oatmeal-pink spray from cheek and hair. Casting the lace trimmed top into the green hamper, switching off the light while my hand brushed the pink inset of the open wall. Always my hands on the stairs as I climbed, trying not to wake him.

I clawed at my lips one day, wanting to punish her for keeping us there. But I'd cut myself before I met him, flung my body down a staircase, sipped codeine pills with liquor so as to silence the one within. What causes this, I wondered, slipping easily into the inherited role, for what we ask for life will show us. And somehow when the body became too heavy to lift from the sheets, I thought myself eccentric. Suffering had chosen me as it had chosen no other. Here was blackness so foreign that it could only be some divine conjuring, something that had picked me out. The martyr in me shrieked for joy, and the will to protect myself gave out on the floor of my bedroom where I was to discover what it was to have a boy move through me into his own pleasure, to push parts of me out of the way while holding onto the breasts of a body quietly perspiring, a voice within saying I don't love you to myself. It was done in punishment. And if it happened again I'd prefer to be drunk and shut the pretty one off in a room somewhere down the hall or in the basement and let sex with her beautiful curves, sex in a pair of white cotton panties littered with cornflowers, be done.

aurora. These memories stir what within would harm her again.
conscience. This is human. It cannot be any other way. You cannot skip parts.

And like that something within rattled. I drank my-self into bed, confining something else...

conscience. So is the story of human evolving, an or-ganism bringing itself into awareness.
aurora. If I have been chosen, then what chose me?
conscience. You have chosen yourself.

The meteor shower, and the light being who crept past the stairs to hang herself in front of the dresser, the rescuers worn thin. One knew it would be like this...

conscience. There are only the answers we seek.

I sought darkness. Once I felt it within, I wanted to

know it. What power it had that all of what I had been could turn dull. That life could be tedious, that I might not choose to rise one day, that I might will death to come at night as a prayer. That pain could be such that it could masticate a spirit.

And I would die here slowly, so that when it finally came time to leave, there could only be crawling and a self so divided we could no longer fend for her. For whom? What center did she have, she that let herself be treated so? All that she was scrawled on a page in darkness that proliferated with her gaze, what we seek seeking us. And so I would die here and drag the body off to the edge of a marsh where we would then descend further, body all dark now, cage of wren, flight smudged against a panel of sky, a jar.

And I would know then how many I housed, how many children exist in the self, and how inexhaustible is spirit, how resilient flight, for one might escape as light ascends from flame, seen only reaching, aspiring, ever in ascent. And that image might live in us. Although returned dark, we would have felt something in the glimmer, would have felt something in the dying out, that we had forgotten being dead.

And something would claim us at the base of a page that had not been before, and we would slip beneath it, reaching in the body a terrain of absent song, a dissembled lyric, a strained line pushed into an open chest until it stung with music. There was nothing else then, just this and a strand that in blue light took us apart.

I wanted to know this desolation, why else would I have come? Why else would I have pushed the sky back? Why else would the observer have hung there, exposed, if I had not asked to do it on my own, so that I might see what I had perhaps forgotten?

BOOK I

IF THERE WERE GODS, HOW COULD I ENDURE IT TO BE
NO GOD? THEREFORE, THERE ARE NO GODS.

FRIEDRICH WILHELM NIETZSCHE

A conversation with Conscience, whom Aurora posits is the self in ascension or a future self (a definition that will grow as her understanding grows), leads to the dissolution of time. Aurora is presented with a prophetic book, coming to the end of which she finds herself to be writing. Alone and covered in ash on what could be the surface of a planet destroyed, she becomes conscious of herself as a primordial spirit in the presence of the divine.

2 THE BOOK OF THE PROPHET

It is still winter, a mild one, as mild as the summer and as gray, so we had the winds sweeping through and that burst of temper that sweeps things away. Then the sky cleared, and the sun shone low, as low as the birds kept on lines, well below the level of turbine blades that now rivaled the skyscrapers that remained. Imagine their silver towers and red ribbons, cords strung through the centers of birds, the birds crossing low the sky, wrapping the facades of their red flight cage.

Conscience had made herself louder in some, and the handful of artists and writers free of pharmaceuticals were racked with what could have only been the dark source within. The human animal was trampling itself in tirade, slave to an old patriarchy. I once knew a girl who thought sound belonged to the moon. What would it matter when we ignored the elephants' keen until it was too late, until the electroshock treatments meant to sever memory and redirect their migration to fertile grounds had caused such unrest in the world that the frequency of madness had reached its height. We were mad to begin with, thinking we could temper and cage what around us held our likeness in a frame.

And so the voice in my head became loud, the being who knew me for what I'd become, the self in ascension, the self more me, this, the more realized one, so that I am God in myself and not God.

3 MEMORY AS VISITATION

This is the voice that you hear now, speaking within as a violent blue streak fills the sky and drops into birds at the entrance of memory.

Do you remember? You are miserable here. Why you stay has to do with not knowing that love is only doing what you asked. You cast it on him, that golden facade of the gods.

Count the birds down the wire to the farm house. A man is speaking too in the memory while the bluebirds that have alighted take turns in the bath. In their beauty reprieve from the hurt of hurting him. The rust on their chests is from love, I divine, distracted, watching them in the water, one by one cleansing their hearts. Mine is so torn I cannot not listen when she speaks, but I hear her voice now and know it was in me, speaking its thoughts aside mine.

Leave him, she says again as the cat goes limp in my arms, as I push past words not meant for warning or sway just there in the conscious visit of memory, for there is no reprimand or rebuke or guilt that I stay, just a knowing that I am not ready to accept—or perhaps have accepted and just pushed it further off into future.

I linger in wonder if every time I revisit a memory I am actually transported in mind; every time I go back, every time I trawl the depths, I am there in the mind of the former self, communicating inadvertently what I know. [And later what this would mean for the macro-cosm if we can tap in to a mind at will.]

In the lucidity of hindsight, the flock washes and preens and moves on, not as a sign that he and I should start over, purge the pain from our chests and begin again, but as a visitation to mark liberation. Birds know when it is time.

5 CONSCIENCE

Like this, I have come to see the self on a continuum, Ego keeping it grounded in present but aware of itself as much as it allows, with access to future as well as to past, so that what I refer to as Conscience ('with-knowledge') is a self liberated and more aware, a self more human for having lived, a self more connected, more divine for the breadth of its experience. Conscience is the knowledge of a self that has realized more of itself. It knows what is harmful to that realization and conveys this knowledge as the inner guide. (So you see, it was never about right and wrong.)

To contemplate this conflation of time, this reaching out, the presence of self in self is to consider what it might look like, that voice that is speaking in your mind, what you have grown into.

aurora. But how is that possible? If Conscience is the voice of the future self revisiting the past through the mind, wouldn't this change everything?

conscience. We are awareness, awareness of a world that has known its ending.

I return to the book.

6 THE BOOK OF THE PROPHET

Who had thought to drain the ink from the plains? Who to infuse poison in the rain? And who to stop them when humankind knew better? How like a woman the soft, white flesh of the squid strung along the starboard side, penetrated and leaking out into a yellow sack her inky darkness.

They were collecting it, her pigment so like oil, and pumping it back into the earth as if this might save us. Who had thought to fill the caverns with her warning? To flush what we had drained? And was this why the oceans turned and roiled now? Yet the human beast moved on, trampling itself underfoot, de-masking itself beneath its foot-soles. What strange reserves panic had wrung, setting us all off in stampede, half of us leading the other.

We were filling the crevasses and coves, the pores and pools, and raping what we had drained to cover it up. Do you understand? The oil we had drilled burned off. We were dying.

conscience. So the voice of Conscience grew louder in some. You were one of them.

7 THE TREE

So Conscience is awareness, a part of the self that exists
in the future, but that which has evolved and expanded
and entered another consciousness. How put into words
what is sensed, what I am given awareness of as a
thought synthesized through body? What I imagine now
as a higher power is myself in light. What can be known
when my touch influences everything? When to observe
changes? When my sight, simply casting a glance in one
direction or another, might cause things there to morph
or to blight? I want to know myself. Why we have been
kept here so long stagnant, so long unaware of our
might?

conscience. To fathom is nonsense; you've only to
allow.

conscience. What are you doing?

aurora. I'm trying to detangle the branches, to busy
myself and learn her again. Reach, and here is a live
thing, sap rivers, blood slowed in winter, an animal in
the depths, extremities lopped off. This is what they'd
given us to eat: what had suffered and gone mad. Men
and their killing and mess while we looked on and so
partook for no one stopped them.

conscience. You couldn't by taking them on. One had
only to imagine something else to lead. That was your
job.

Branches tap at pavement, but in my head where sound still resonates, for there is no tar now, no blacktop, no toxic lid to the world. Where Conscience mourns I feel death. The gnat formed in wind. To contemplate such a thing and the ones who took us, what kept us small in fear when to thrive was only to turn the gaze, to observe something else and so affect it into existence. The feeling of being tethered to what hadn't yet grown, what wasn't aware, for even in conversations it was like this, the restlessness, what wanted to play and explore, what wanted to shake the men out of their order, what used all its sex. What am I trying to tell you? What do I see? Detangling with touch that exceeds human, this being which grows and has grown.

In the balance of your idealized perfection, there is no room for the fierceness in me. Envision the world in harmony; something in it feels like a cage. In balance isn't there stagnancy? And so what are we striving for? Couldn't we go on forever exploring? Wouldn't the universe support this?

conscience. So we have designed it, not to be perfect but infinite. Not even to be good. I am everything: an extended conscious awareness that we are larger than what exists, yet we exist within it in part.

8 EVERYTHING HUMAN

I am in this room and I see, but it doesn't see me, here with the men plinking away at their blocks: half of our doubts reflected in the world as our punishment: you, our despots, our gods. We have feared your judgments long enough, Männer! Elated in your concessions, measured ourselves in your frames. "I believe that if a woman succeeds in withdrawing from the mass, or rather raising herself above the mass, she grows ceaselessly and more than a man." Dear God, Schopenhauer! Elitism and privilege, you are what is to be swept off, things from which we grow, errors in thought to be corrected, wrong turns, flatness, plain. Had you taken your head from your own spacious ass, what might you have seen, beyond the pince-nez?

Half of your doubts reflected.

And so I give validation to the unseen, for what is vision when it fails to exceed what befalls it, when it fails to recognize but focuses instead on what can be proven?

Have you never felt what your presence does in the world? Aren't you tired of these things? What shall we draw next? What next shall we be? Now that we have done everything human.

All of this wickedness happening and we looking on, and then there was change, something rising up not in destruction, but I dare say love, love the color of an emerald bridge stretching out into a landscape. What happened was at once feminine and divine. But can I say that it wasn't a force that didn't somehow ally itself with some yang thing, some penetrant cyclical thing? It was not.

Ω

In crouch threat a crane collapses before the wind, unfolding its wings over the ground. It forgets not that this world exists within us as much as we exist within the world; it considers everything and claims it. What sort of world would it be that took heed?

Imagine a bird cleansing itself, preening its pinions so that what runs off into the earth destroys it. This is not who I am. How would it look not to poison and maim? How can we fly without burning?

conscience. How can we recognize what doesn't recognize itself? Open your eyes and get to the tree, the river beneath you in tremulous gush. Move. Move on in conversation, move through this room like a séance or prayer, an incantation.

aurora. Oh that thing in me afraid to hit the page for it knows a bird that is empty. You were showing me how it was done: I was to clip the strings, the ribbons yellowed in sun, orange tracks beneath fraying thread. Bones, thimbles that we'd break and wish that we had no longer done this, boots sifting through dust and debris. How long linger, how long the sun at the rim?

9 GRAY

Conscience takes the hand of the ragged thing sifting white dust from the street, the girl I will always be romping in a dress with torn sleeves, hair neglected.

aurora. Why would I not die here? Countenance hung. Birds hung. Parched yellow rags tucked into alcoves and the knotted gray of what was. How could I not die here when death is in you, when I smell it in the ashen leaves, when you are perhaps not made of light but gray?
conscience. Gray what?
aurora. Gray. Let go of my arm.
conscience. You go on. It is why you've come. To witness is to wear the body. It is heavy but you go on. We can spend a fortnight or a thousand. You can ruminate, or I can drag.
aurora. How could we have done this?
conscience. Oh, you know.
aurora. Have mercy for a minute. We're all dead.
conscience. But *you* are not unless you choose this, and you don't.
aurora. Then why show me?
conscience. Because you dally. It is in you, yet you rest. Feel my dead.

10 GLASS

I drop the hand which skids into a pile of concrete. There are safe houses within where we go. Stay in the safe house. Stay in the safe house. Eyes closed. The safe house is upstairs in the body, upstairs where we cannot feel, upstairs, cerebral, upstairs.

There is a glass hand through my heart, or my heart is glass and the hand; everything transparent and fragile, already shattered and yet intact, depending on where the mind concentrates. Shards, and we are on this street in a room that keeps opening out until it is rubble, all white debris, ash.

conscience. Now do you understand?
aurora. How we can be both future and past?
conscience. Does it matter when it is done?
aurora. You brought me here.
conscience. We are the same.

conscience. So is the push of peasants into the current, so is rain and bodies caught in trees full of blood, and yesterday a sky so pink with ruin so late that night had turned within belly-up, the moon an eye cataract in its dead-flesh sky. Vision was elsewhere, vision in the limbs and in the hands and upstairs in the chamber of head and heart sans physicality, everything connecting speaking back to itself, you, the microcosm of the cosmos, terrified of the god in yourself, ascending. There is a coldness in that, a loneliness in the one who must lead; blue water where the trail ends...

11 A GOD THAT WOULD LIVE

aurora. Opaque blue and my blue white feet stepping off into the snow toward the ridge. I remember. Over the city how sky was rent and leaked out and became release. And there I was dashed into a streak and sounded like a chord. How could I settle into body? How could I sit still when I leapt when light leapt across the panes, slamming red against the window and rattling the façade; when sandstone chipped from turret scuttered across the floor; when blown back in the drapes and wreathing around, you were braiding my core in flight?

conscience. Beauty strapped to the air, her own hands clutching the wooden form, holding tight to the brackets while shattering loose, looping a dissonant maddening hymn with a timbre from beyond. She is scrawling something across the flight cage. She is fevered and pink and alive: a city of birds wrapping their towers: a god that would live this time.

Where was the room that contained you? The vessel, the body, where could that be? And do you remember the child who'd crept out onto the rooftop? Remember how a city became two cities, red clay roofs reminiscent of what we would see. Do you remember what it was in her that flung her from the window and onto the ledge, the thin sliver of awning and the artist's hand crushing her back...

aurora. You urging me out, saying to me run while I

ran my hands over the sand because I wasn't listening. Because I'd become so recalcitrant as to defy even self.

    conscience. Are you listening now?

    aurora. —

    conscience. And so it was then. But now?

Magpies scour the leaf bed, clambering over the scourge.

conscience. Hold your tail aloft, they have come to say and, take, take, crepitating in droves. Take, take what is yours. They have been sent for you and from you. Do you understand? Don't you feel that? Go!

aurora. And what shall I do? What would you have me do?

conscience. What you have done (while the machines pulse in your chair, while the workmen force up the street and slip their tubing under there). This is what killed us, remember?

BOOK 2

I BELIEVE THAT MOST OF WHAT WAS SAID
OF GOD WAS IN REALITY SAID OF THE SPIRIT
WHOSE BODY IS EARTH.

GEORGE WILLIAM RUSSELL (Æ)

THE SOUL OF THE SOUL IS GOD.

KARL VON ECKARTSHAUSEN

As Aurora reflects on the apocalyptic scene and takes inventory, Conscience guides her through memory that she might recognize her own perfection within a world governed by error. Throughout, it becomes evident that this omnipresent figure has accompanied her all along. Just what it is seems to be evolving with her expanding awareness. Is it God? Encouraged to assume so, she opens to its revelations, which culminate when she recognizes its powers are her own.

1 DISCARDED

I crawl back into bed dragging dead things: bird wings, red like the thread, music ground into the ground and nothing else; the bombed out cars would have taken place in another scene. Here was just powder gray as dismal as a snow sky in spring, short-lived hope, beauteous white quickly melted down the river below the Arch. For as long as I can't conjure anything else, the coin is flipped and possibility shattered.

The mind rattles on. So it began with discarding. What would she get rid of? There were the old shoes and hats and things the world had worn when she was the someone else she thought she should be. The teacher's attire, how one dressed when she adopted a profession, metal sling-backs, a rusted match, three hoary clogs printed with the text of doomsday, a violent violet footprint through the center of the barrister's yard, three turtledoves decked in rose twigs, so they couldn't fly. Rattling and stomping and excavation, and here again that dripping squid held aloft. The desolation in finding oneself alive among a colossus of artificial things.

conscience. Stop denying what you are.

Just as you knew you would leave him, you know you will do this, you know you have craft. Do not berate yourself again for the time it takes to put on courage. Get up, and you will find it easier to be who you are than to deny.

aurora. But it is not easy to rise against...

conscience. Then rise into something. Rise into yourself as a god.

2 THE GOD LOST IN OURSELVES

...a communion of spirit, a transference of energy, power, might, a belief in oneself as part of a god so complex she can never truly know herself, who lives to remember what she is capable of, who strives toward ascending human form, while finding requisite this vessel of containment. We are a culmination of God, God wanting to know itself, so that God is not human or animal or resembling any such thing, but God in all. God is the earth as much as a dragonfly, black space as much as a fingernail or a ray of sun, the sun as well as the feeling of love. What can we learn? How can we ascend? Where is the meaning in striving?

conscience. Our cosmos expands, our being unfolds exponentially in what we're made aware. Your task, your mission is to seek yourself into existence and so grow God, grow our capabilities, our power in intention, for what proceeds now does so in chaos.

aurora. Yet in that chaos is system and law for wouldn't it have to be ordered?

conscience. Be. Live this realized self into existence as if there were an end, as if the goal were attainable. There is so much we cannot fathom in our current state that to push it might extend our form, might evolve our species that the conception of space might be fathomable. Evolution, ascension, call it what you will, we are here to expand and to grow. As much as you are an individual asserting its individuality, you are symbiotic, necessary to the growth of what we together are.

aurora. Thus, the universe, is an ever evolving mysterium. As soon as it's created, the cosmos multiplies out of our comprehension. We are the God lost in ourselves, what we've created having staggered out of our control, out of our bidding and alive for us to explore. With each human birth and the birth of each star, God branches out of control. And yet we come to a time when things have been stunted.

The world is still the same around me, the one that I see, the physical one. The other is changing.

conscience. The mind of God has changed.

aurora. All along to have been with you and not to have known it. I know now what I've concealed. Do we not all feel it, rising in our being like what has been dormant too long? What could only hibernate in the recesses until discovered into existence. The ship on the ocean, the flat sea, the orb in the sky that's not round but a hole.

Here the jar is shaken again, what is in it contained.

conscience. When have you stopped seeking the god in yourself? Why are you stunted and sad?

aurora. Is it this that keeps me destitute in the rubble, prodded and lamed by my innermost thoughts, that there's something of cynicism in the world? Depression is the bell jar; the feeling we can't achieve whatever it is we're seeking; the feeling there's no need for ourselves.

conscience. It is worthlessness and muck. Beyond

the jar is everything. Every happiness you've imagined, every dream you've ever dreamed. And their opposites, if you choose. But here is possibility.

3 SYNTHESIS

conscience. There is a world inside you've conjured. Go on. Your world does not die here, for you are connected. Without vessel we cannot know ourselves. We cannot skip steps. We are constantly evolving this thing, but just what that evolution entails you cannot yet fathom, for as consciousness expands so expands human capacity for knowledge of this sort. Attention to metaphysical realms enhances your capacity, but the attention is distracted. You are necessary to changing the focus. What do you imagine of me?

aurora. Synthesis. The world is a shared idea. We are a part of that which must assert itself to overcome the imbalance which will inevitably destroy us.

conscience. We are awareness, awareness of a world that has known its ending.

aurora. Yes.

conscience. What we fear has already happened and so there is no fear.

On another plane it is different. We live another plane of existence. I know you as feminine. I am what you are aware of, as you say.

aurora. I am listening this time.

conscience. Think in terms of how I communicate with you, only now you have knowledge of a conscious intention in that being, think in terms of processes and what thrives in the natural world.

4 ASYLUM

It was a morbid day. The sky was blue with wet, the General Store rain-sopped and depressed as far as pale wood could look depressed, but it hadn't turn cold until the conversation turned, until the comment about my avocation and then the slight and the strained look of the academic looking out from cerebral heights. Pathos, he thinks dismissively, handing off the equipment: a pair of binoculars, clipboard, and control sheet. He lets the spoon fall against the back of the cup, swirls the dregs, believes he's had enough.

conscience. The obvious psychological conclusion here would be that you used the scientist to play out one of your dramas, to pattern the irresponsible dreamer. But the more beautiful and so more truthful story would have occurred beneath it all. You were feeling everything from the rain to the scientist's judgment.

We were bid entrance by a man named Beau dragging his hand through the damp morning air, parting the mist like a man of God in the sign of a cross over each of us. He, who would remove my hero facade as quickly as I endowed him with it, gave us a rather uninspired tour of the grounds. One could see that he didn't understand why we were volunteering and what it would mean to us in the end.

We were there to observe the crane species in conservation, kept to replenish those endangered in the wild. We were there to carry witness in the body, to feel the birds within us. Beau admitted he was conflicted. Some days he wondered why he didn't slit the cages and set the birds free. After all what sense did it make that some were chosen to suffer beneath a net sky, here, until they were called on.

What if I could promise you asylum for your colts? I said one day to the birds.

They are birds, Poet.

Bird people. I felt immediately dumb. I didn't belong with aviculturists and ornithologists. Beau hunted with a falcon. The sky filled with golden light as he told us. In the shadows of the hills a man, thigh thick with suede, releases a raptor from his arm on an ivory cord. It sweeps out over the roost of eagles and snares a rabbit from the brush then returns, Yeats streaming from the tether, and the romance of...

"I sleep with dogs," Beau says on which his clothes exude a doggy smell that peppers the air and draws in thick around him and his shaggy, dark, oily hair and the fossils of bird tracks in his skin. He is tired and just a man. Like this, I keep getting it wrong.

The banter in the main room didn't concern us. Scientists haggling each other, cajoling and bamboozling. Uncomfortable to say the least—"I will miss your riveting riposte, Joel."

I scratched at my neck where some flat hives were breaking out. Even within the English Department, where I taught, I could never quite bring myself to engage in such speak. We had cages to clean, birds to feed.

The facility consisted of a dirt road grid connecting 60 pens. It took about two hours to complete the task using a donated van whose back doors swung open behind us, so that the food buckets had to be fastened to the walls with bungee cords.

aurora. We are the birds! If I can imagine the netting I can remove it, and so we traverse the terrain of memory together, you, trying to make me aware of what I've lived.

conscience. Not what you lived, but how you were only half or quarter there. You caged yourself, but it was all inside. You knew things you weren't yet using. Even the proclivity to mythologize men. This is godlike, not wrong. The men were too small for you to love them.

I am alone when I enter the cage. The whooping crane, gaze skyward, slides its head down its back and prostrates itself in the dirt before me. I watch in awe of its graceful obeisance then step forward to finish my tasks.

Continue, unheeded, to move past this bird and what happens unfolds disjunctively; its limbs snap erect, it darts forward, it jabs its beak at the hands, drawing blood and white fear as I hold the fodder bucket between us as shield.

I see my hands cut from the chipped beak; feel the lachrymose face beneath that spared, my body sway as the van bumps from the compound over the red sand.

5 ONE MIND

I am aware, I say, opening and allowing things to drift in and out of consciousness and my life. Things do not always happen in earthly ways. Although we are human interacting as human, we are vulnerable to energies, unseen forces, ideas, things coming through unconventional channels.

I was counting eagles for – Council, which was why the scientist and I had met for coffee that dreary day. He would have labeled me irresponsible. I would have felt his disinterest in the site where I'd been stationed. I would have sensed its unimportance in his eyes, and this would have been enough to turn me away, to convince me to shirk my responsibilities, for eventually I stopped going. I no longer reported in. It did not matter; perception encompasses other things. I live informed by what takes no verbal cue. That day, he released me from the responsibility nonverbally. It was understood beyond us. I cannot explain.

"I released you and insulted you. Don't forget that," he says now in mind.

But you weren't in touch with the part of you that had decided on a level below the human one. Oh how do I explain? You were inhabiting the superficial realm of mere appearances. Where you saw a capricious young coquet, an unfocussed dreamer, what else could you have thought? You scorned me, and labeled me flighty and naïve, you, the small-town scientist, provincial in manner and expectation, limited beyond cerebral scope. I wanted to like you. I wanted to mythologize you like I did all my men: Environmental Scientist and Hero observing the staggering sum of eagles returned. My site had been replenished. You said it yourself, dismissing me in the moment you dismissed it. My interest dwindled, as you knew it would if you had listened within on that level of self that knows things, that level on which we communicate as one organism perhaps.

So that it was not my intention to be irresponsible, just to trust this other level of self so intimately that I would sacrifice the phenomenal as I do. Repeatedly. As a fault.

What happens beneath us on the level of god? We feel, react, so many things happening in the multichambered organism.

6 ASH, PRESCIENCE, THE EARTH BODY

White ash falls on the afternoon. Know it as augur. *Not war. Not war.* Yet ash meant burning and burning meant deliberation and deliberation in this case meant war—a bomb going off over the city. What else could explain it? Ash falling from the sky, light on the breath of a god... Don't speak of it, and it will retreat into the nothingness from which such visions emerge.

Was there meaning beyond? A connection to my life? The sight evoked no emotional response other than awe at the beauty of a summer snow, flakes languidly falling against the pink glow of a centuries-old brick wall, a sense of communion with what is divine. But fear came in the corollary as the mind attempted sense.

You've only to allow, a voice tells me.

Weeks later again on a clear sky, downy, white flakes fill the empyrean. Grímsvötn releases a red bird. This is God: this foreknowledge, the connection to an omniscient force. I can listen, not listen, to the tectonic movement of mind.

7 OTHER REALMS

There is a man in my kitchen observing me for the few short seconds it takes me to lift my eyes from the bathroom floor that I'm cleaning with an old pink sock. Before I can behold him he's gone, his dark gray and silver uniform receded through realms. I do not know him, yet I am not afraid. Curiosity drew him. There is fierceness as was with the angel or daemon, a fierceness of knowledge that wields its might, a trait I intend to assume.

conscience. As you master these things it draws more. The greater your vision the more you will see until other presences make themselves visible to you.
aurora. Like the man in the kitchen.
conscience. That was Niesad. He wanted to give you something.

As soon as I get to the outskirts, I'm free. But there is still confinement in what backs the yard, in the hectare patch of trees called forest. This place is refuge, but not its own. Birds can lower their voices, though the faint din of machine is still there. I run and am caught, an arm's length from city wherever I turn. Where is the wilderness I knew? Where is a forest in which I can get lost, in which I can lose myself, in which something speaks not in reaction, but in its own way? In which something speaks that is not human.

I know that voice, but it is not here. All I have of that realm I've collected of hallucinations, of hypnagogic figures held aloft in the light. Now as my attention turns, as I desire to see, they are coming and making their world known to me.

conscience. You were on the cusp. It was why we were able to find you, existing there, expectantly, as if something had told you to wait. We are God, doesn't this change everything?

aurora. But there must be something greater to be known. There must be sense and a system that I do not control. For how can it be that I control so much? That what I seek seeks me, that I am a part of God, that my discoveries multiply in ratio to my expansion? In expansion is growth and so metamorphosis. So what is to be known?

conscience. Explore.

What of that place within the body of darkness? That place of human suffering that felt somehow the center of all, that felt somehow where suffering might end and a new thing begin? That felt the place of existence where God began in us?

8 A PROPHET

Perhaps it is part of a story, a myth one needs to tell herself to proceed. We begin in chaos for here it is we have a task: put order to the world. Set it right in your mind, and the external world unfolds. The blank page unbearable, so that here you have a cluttered mess of ideas, everything tangling and strangling each other out. There are only solutions.

It is the not knowing. Having abilities but not knowing how to use them, and if I am using them the way they were intended. And if there is intent then whose?

Within there is a guide. The more I listen the better I can hear her, but there are other voices as well, darker voices grown of the past, before I knew I could stop them, before I knew to bring them into the world would mean they would grow of their own volition. Samael.

What we have done we draw forth from the cosmos. But it is not as I'd originally thought, for everything is constantly evolving, that vision that impels action is mutable. I set forth on a path that alters it, and yet it is altered into something greater, always something greater, so that as I strive to achieve, I achieve more. The more we discover the more there will be to be discovered, but we have kept ourselves small in this universe. We have said to the God, take this, shhhhh. That God has gone mad in us, kept in its cage, yet God can never be caged. *A glint of light in the periphery.*

What when that realm breaks open on this?

You are still seeking a prophet. I am here, says inside.

aurora. It happens less often but still it happens: something shakes the bough, and there is fear and forgetting and self-doubt.

conscience. It is why we have a sign from them.

aurora. But from whom?

conscience. It does not matter.

"Choose a sign," the woman says. She is in a tent at a craft fair. I do not think she knows what she says, unadorned, the words that she speaks. There is no bird that alights on her shoulder, that violet macaw heard in the wings. There is no mystique other than a plain-clothed nun, trading her wares in parade. This is no gypsy or mystic. What then takes her mouth and fills it with what I need?

9 GOD AND THE FOREST

There is a woman an ocean to my left who thinks governing means destruction, paving a way: a black-top of riverbeds, armies of men, farmland of wild naked will, defunct seed. There is a place in her charge where a part of me lives in a monkey tanning its ass on a fir tree. There is an animal I call myself who swings and bites and shatters the limbs of the jobowa-blo. He has a clock in his belly There are creatures of my own creation that have lines on their bellies that pointed at the sun will charge.

If everything I can imagine possibly exists, it is in a land ungoverned by men.

There is a river that sees itself in the light that morphs on the underside of leaves. When it tires of knowing itself in this way, it will be night, and I will emerge from its waters, mighty and uncontained. How I love my eyes and my hands and how light I've become in quest, for here I trail out over the sky. There is a disc in my heart, a wedge of axe that I carry. It reminds me to touch and not turn away; it reminds me there are more than five of these mountains.

I know what she looks like, this sovereign, this woman an ocean to my left, and I know that her children will be lame. I am one of her children, and I want to see the forest. I want to meet the bird that makes it rain. Does she not see that the soul is housed? Does she not see how laughter falls into soy fields, and then there is silence as it passes away like sand in a hiss that turns the blood cold? The snake will lame her children. And one will be trapped in the forest, where they have burned things like animals escaping.

Ω

Why would I let you take these things? I ask her, for I will not feel like dying. That was a house long ago. I will not have to explain, for in you, you will know. And I believe in you, I say. I believe in the woman in your head who is not me but who speaks of things that are universal while you bock and sway and call in the guards.

Today the guards are dowdy, and I will spring from the forest in a perfume that leads them so far into the past they cannot rise. They will sleep in their chairs on the terrace, and no one will notice them for the spell of rain that falls and scatters the servants' attention as they lower the shades and swing closed the panes. And you and I will have silence enough for the both of us. How unused to listening you are, you with your ego and headstrong ways, you, bombarding with bombast, master of the masculine, you, only half of your rule.

Retired to the back of the parlor, we only now notice the quietude within.

When you speak, what you say is in the voice of the toucan and that silly grey beast that brays at the dawn. What you share is of a day when you were eleven, walking alone at the edge of the bog, when the river warned you of the lemur stalking your song. Cries stretch long in your telling and wider the hole in the burlap bag hung over your shoulder tug on a nail as the song grows worn and frail.

Like this, I could be a god entering your head, but what right do I have? To temper your will and impose my own? A god does not ask this of herself.

But I have saved the life of the forest.

10 A PLACE OF GREAT SUFFERING

On the underside of all, there is a place of great suffering. This might have been what they had meant by hell. In any case, it is a place you carry inside you, the access of which is dread. The depressed know it well, for they align with it until it hollows out their center and spreads a dark expanse within. Exploring is to become its darkness, so that surfacing is to know the body as something else. What we are, what we feel of a physical self is torn from the center and replaced with void. Void being vacuous, void being dark, void causing one to call out in pain. But the voice ringing, too, is vacuous, erasing as it speaks what we are, erasing parts into space, black holes, what was contained now streaming out into what has not been collected into form.

This is where the forest goes to suffer. It is not in punishment.

In the transport of memory, I know what is to come, not as a story that someone has told me, but as what I have lived and will live.

Like this, I open the book I have not completely written up to a future page. I see my life, the splendor of it, and feel this thing reaching out and touching the inside of things from the space inside us all, where we reside when we are quiet and know ourselves as one. For us to thrive, you must thrive. Do not let us die.

Wake up. We're not dead.

But I don't know how to do this, I don't know what to do, but the things within cry act, act like the sky splendent above, break open this time. Cast off the jar, break out of the net. What does it look like? Oh my god to live. That bird inside is wild. She needs a purpose, the world will say. To fly, man. To fly. It's no more complicated than that. Bat your wings. Take off. Let the child loose to explore. We don't have a clue what human is.

I have to remember the man in myself, not to be caged. He was only doing what I'd asked.

Child, fly. That's it. Our focus was wrong.

And now in the devastation we're all depressed, and there is a scientist hopping around in a lab coat trying to catch mice to tell us how to fix it. I take his hand—he's frantic—the hair on it that was curly and red, half gone. Somewhere within he knows the truth. Using mice to tell us how the brain works?

Close your eyes. Be still. Feel the plates within slide, how something dense moves in. We are the earth inside.

11 WAX WINGS

Darkness will always have its way. When I ask what it is, it shows me. There are worlds within that know. But light. Have we asked? Isn't that what brought the dark things? Antitheses keeping things in flux. Discontent and rage.

conscience. There are things you can't yet know. What you had imagined communing from another realm is the self cast out of its body. What you will do you can only imagine.

aurora. —

conscience. You know things about us, that there is more than one. You know I am mighty; you know we go on. What do you see?

aurora. It is more what I sense, that I am part of what will shift us so far along that we cannot be contained in a body, or at least not this human form. Our scope here is limited, our vision, our capacity to understand the universe to which we belong. Fixated on an image of beauty we fall into ourselves and keep falling until we cannot move beyond. We drown in the pool and keep drowning. Let us move the monkey. Don't you want to grow?

Some of us are developing other senses. We know things before they occur; see things that we will become. Yet when one so vehemently disagrees with its society what right does it have to belong? I have lived removed, thinking it at times a fault but wanting nothing more of a human life.

This time the martyr lives, my sister said. She'd channeled the thought somehow but couldn't apperceive how it would resonate within me, for what comes through others towards us is in answer to our need.

This is how the universe works. All that is beyond, all that is uncontrollably beyond, what we cannot alter or influence, what we cannot explain without rendering dull with categorization and definition and a lexicon that fails us, is within on an eternal plane. I go there to know what it feels like to close my human eyes and see. I go there to know what hears beyond my human ears, what beats beyond my human heart, what feels beyond skin, what senses and tastes and what conjures what it perceives beyond. What need have I for bull and bear? For method and degree and organization? I surrender and know all, not as a thought but experience, revelation, gnosis.

In the deep heavy heat of the south land, a storm begins to blow.

conscience. Do you see how you must destroy everything? Do you see how hatred spawns what comes next?

aurora. It is not hatred but a wild thing seeking the place it belongs. It is not here for what you do to me.

conscience. You can't keep escaping container.

aurora. But I've exhausted its capacity. I must cast it off.

conscience. That is death.

aurora. I am beyond death. I enter the one beyond me, the one I become, unhindered from what we are.

What does it mean to go forward?

conscience. It means not to be afraid to tell me who you are. What do you want? What do you see?

aurora. Flight. Release, and me kicking off the old and entering a new form.

conscience. What do you want?

aurora. I want to lead. I want to discover something new. I want to explore. I want never to make myself small again.

conscience. Enter that impulse to release, to empty to cleanse to purge to let go control.

aurora. You want me to open what lies rent in a field years from here, a rack of wings torn. I will not open these places again. I will not come here to display, if I can help it at all, the crescent in my chest, this waning hole. In the bath the birds and the heart, rust a color that splinters in things. And I am dragged soft as a heart through its sediment, vulnerable as an instrument sawed off, metal flute or swan harp I swallow as cage. What dare carry wind here? What dare ask a flap of skin that tender closing? Will I need you? What am I wrong?

Then there is the Grief God putting to bed what should not be awake in these things, what must no longer inhabit what it did.

And so I go forward and backward like an artist over the river, traversing a page like wire, trying to figure out how to stand on my own and how to cross, when to cross means to lead. Slack in the wire, a figure bent over backwards and flailing his arms, a pole for balance, a girl on his shoulders, another, the clapping within trees on the banks of the Danube. The whole scale of human has a place at the riverside where the acrobats trickle across the water in festival.

Ω

I will become the one fallen who then rises and says I know how it is to fly high. I know what it is to burn wax into my skin from the sun. I know what it is to scrape my belly along the gravel path. Did we die when we fell into the sea? No one sees how I have been fashioned out of one saved until I rise and show you what it is to behold your world while knowing something other.

A thing like that thinking itself human. Through the crack under the sink I watch them crawl in the light, what is not there if I were to look again. How I write around and around and around the story until the pieces that were hardly visible duplicate themselves, and I can make out a pattern.

conscience. We were flying remember? Someone warned us down.

12 COLLAPSE OF TIME

aurora. Who are you?

conscience. What you grow into. But our growth is simultaneous. Allow your sense of time to collapse. It is less that we intersect at points than that our growth influences and alters all at once. Remain with your image of the traveling conscience for a moment. Let us say it is like this. Who you are now enters a memory. It lives again the embarrassment, the shame, the glee,—in the case of the poison ivy, the loneliness and despair—and you are there. Your consciousness is the presence of Conscience. This Conscience, or more developed self, is what gives us a sense that we are doing right or wrong. Its assessment and judgment are automatic, for it contains within it knowledge of the repercussions experienced beyond the event. As soon as we're transported in mind, (and it isn't really transport or travel, but these words will have to do) experience travels with us, within our conscious awareness, so that we are perceiving past through what we now know.

Therefore, the more you travel in memory, the more you re-visit the past, the more aware you become and the more that experience grows, not just where you are in time, but also where you were, and where you will go. Essentially, the more you become aware of yourself beyond spatiotemporal confines, the greater you become and the greater your presence in the world and thus the world's consciousness.

Come. Take a situation in its simplest form: a young woman, a romantic, a dreamer, living in a house with a man her opposite, world-worn, practical. She is bored with him and their life. She doesn't yet realize that love is an energy she conjures between them. She wants to save him—how you all want to save and be saved! Conversely, her energy and passion have the effect of shutting him down, so that he no longer touches her, which confuses and depresses her and makes her want to die.

This is the memory you will enter to know why.

They are doing yard work one day in early spring when she tugs on a vine at the edge of the woods and ends up covered head to toe in a rash. You remember how the vine slid through your hands and packed its poison there beneath the skin so that you thought you'd go mad with it.

aurora. He'd made me feel uncomely, but my god, I was so beautiful then!

conscience. And the garden was there in assistance, everything around you surrounding that belief.

aurora. Unwittingly, I spread the oil until my skin blistered and swelled and stank, until it yellowed and cracked and pooled. How beautiful the body in defence and how beautifully horrific I'd become, for he had made me feel untouchable until everything around me succumbed.

How many times I've revisited this memory to see it as completely as I do now.

conscience. Yet our beliefs are not one-fold. We are desirous of a thousand things all at once. You were lonely and desirous of love. And in the heat of the shower as you sought relief from the itch, it multiplied in an orgasmic rush that racked the body, heat drawing out histamine in release. Wave upon wave drenched the body in pain, drenched in burn, drenched in a tearing off of skin, an animal lust, a thousand percussive flush in which we fear that we will die, it's just too much. The sickness, the life, how everything can be all at once wanting to bare everything.

So that our environment responds and extends us. We're always in communion with what is beyond.

aurora. And yet I was going mad.

conscience. You were going mad for loneliness.

aurora. Leave him, you said, when the cat went limp in my arms. She was all I had, stretched across realms, a being who knows the otherworld. The tenderness, the plea in it for what it conveys of the self reaching out to self to say don't go.

And so the cat becomes the one within, the one we stow away, dying in us. *Light in the periphery.*

conscience. Stay down. This is not who I am, you said then. I am not one who gets treated like this.

aurora. Yet I was like this, insolently pushing past you, cat in hand. *Leave him.* It is as we are now as a world ignoring Conscience, for who are we to destroy but ourselves?

And so I am God in myself and not God. You are feeding me with insight that I cannot hold, have no place to fit for I haven't lived this part yet.

Here, a self reaches itself through memory, seeking for answers, revisiting a mood, but not wanting that self to turn around, not expecting that it could, not knowing it might respond.

If I were to listen, wouldn't it alter what comes

next?

conscience. What we fear has already happened, so there is no fear.

aurora. –

conscience. Don't be afraid of dying, for in dying there is life.

aurora. But I don't want to be part of the destruction.

Ω

conscience. I am also growing. Can you conceive of this? That I might have just reached this awareness. That your growth increases our awareness of each other, and so our consciousness. Oh, I do not know how it works, only that I can send you things by thinking you might find them useful. And yet, it is not a cognitive response.

aurora. Oh my god, the snake! If in revisiting a memory, I am actually transported in mind, then I have brought the birds and the ivy; I, the snake and leviathan. It would have been my doing.

conscience. I wanted to touch you. I wanted you to know something else existed, that I was here. And here was divinity reaching out to claim what it had conjured, to urge it on, so that I am the environment as well, what is responding to you somehow under my command like cells.

I am the god in love with you, in love with the feminine nature of myself, whose hands touch you everywhere, who is water and a rash and a man filling you.

aurora. Of course it would be like this. To fathom the mysterious and push it aside, to peak under veils and let them drop and drop and become unfathomable again.

The pendulum, the animals, the visions in light: all ways of communicating with myself.

13 DECEPTION

There is a snake in the yard playing dead for me, its tongue hung from its mouth like a rag. Step closer, and it rises up, thickening its neck like a cobra. Zero at the bone, so that I run into the house thinking I've narrowly escaped with my life.

But cobras in Wisconsin? I've been deceived by the Eastern Hognose, a serpent offering nothing more insidious than a headbutt if you don't yield. Its message, though I won't realize it until I've already slept with him: the actor you've befriended is a perfidious liar.

What did Jung say? 'I don't believe in God, I know.'

conscience. Go on. All of this is you. All that surrounds, the mistakes we make not listening, not heeding the warnings we've drawn...

14 GROWING GOD

aurora. Are you doing this?

conscience. Belief is, our belief that something is aiding us, that something beyond wants us to know it exists.

aurora. Entanglement. Ask any woman in touch with her soul voice, and she will explain what the world attempts through science, what they encode and decode with their third participant, and their colliding and exploding and hacking.

I can hear the thoughts of those who intersect my path. I know things before they manifest in any measurable form. Like this, I know if we were to come into our power the current world could not exist, for we have advanced below its surface and outgrown it, like a skin or chrysalis.

Is it you in my eyes now? Am I other?

conscience. It is the ship again on the horizon, what our eyes aren't trained to see.

aurora. Why do I keep thinking about clothing? Why should the body be different in any way?

conscience. You won't want to think of that. What radiation might do to a child.

aurora. There was to be no horror.

conscience. But wouldn't it be necessary for something? You are no longer human. You are the storm. Be the storm, your will not to destroy but to liberate, to expand. Isn't that what draws you along? Isn't it why the cycle is a sign it is done? There is something else to pursue.

aurora. Is this why we move the planet? Oh how cruelly we destroy ourselves! until an elephant might no longer appeal with its last wisps of breath with a trumpeting herald of fight. Gabriel is this elephant thrown to the ground, its legs hacked from haunch. Can we not hear his plight? What in us suffers we have consumed of an animal tortured alive.

Oh I want to fly out of that window and know a soul uncontained! Would I know then how to serve her?

15 THE ONE WITHIN

Ideas come through that are beyond my knowing. It is as if what I sought sought to further itself, to expand, as if I were continuing what I had once undertaken. And it is this expanding that refutes the cyclical idea of time, so that time does not concern me. It is this: why your ideas come from within and spill onto the floor like leaves from my mouth. And these ideas that I read or come across, did they exist in the author's head, or is it only in mine that he lived it? Either way I do not like this tail-eating dragon, this snake. Is it construct? Have you set it before me as prey? Shall I devour myself and move on.

conscience. You can't. You are created anew. That is the point.

aurora. When is cycle not a cat chasing its tail?

conscience. We cannot escape expansion. What we have is beyond our comprehension. If we could fathom the ignorance of a disappeared measure of time, then we would know ourselves ascended, and we would know our world destroyed. And there in this place you speak of, in that inexhaustible well, we might meet, and I think we have, but not as human, no never as human...

aurora. For then I would be female.

conscience. There is no female/male in the well, no body.

aurora. Then why had we chosen these parts in the world?

Thrusting thrusting the black bird is male—and yet from within it is not. She is darkness unveiled and recovered. If it makes you feel bad; it isn't true, the angel said, and I keep returning here, for what we have created we recognize. And we, the collective below my surface, who I am when I enter the depths, what speaks to me, all that has been, and with what I attempt now to enter the future... But it is not an attempt. We are here.

conscience. Yes, and like this future becomes past; white powdery dust, the forest. This was the papier-mâché, the ash you had seen wet with storm. Do you see now how they correspond? That it was a memory of the future, a future dream you entered when you'd left the world. What you'd created within to sustain you. The story of the hero dashed hard against the walls, hurling herself into the cove. And all of the voices of rabbits were yours here and all of the snakes in the path, rivulets dripping as the world was tipped and the masks spilled their contents into the sea.

This thing that you are is larger than you, but you contain it. You are its creator. It is why you are so respectful of the process of unfurling, why you let what is exist around you uncontrolled, why you observe without the will to impose. It is your desire that lives and creates of what you see around you its tale.

Aphorisms speak at times a specious cadence, the dissembler hides within the words. But what if he didn't know himself for a dissembler?

16 THE PLACE OF ALL-KNOWING

aurora. When we fly from the window and break into spirit, we become what is no longer contained. But am I still human, for I cannot imagine it?

conscience. Oh, but you can. The voices that speak come from others. Although you hear them in your mind, they're not yours. What would you imagine contains them? How could they penetrate your thoughts if they must transport with them container?

aurora. But they do not come from a voice but a well. Is ours the same? An archetype I've borrowed? And how can I have borrowed? How can it not be mine if it came from the place of my mind?

conscience. Cling not to form; cling not even to person, but be, and your body will become what is neither governed nor defined but known in and of itself and so becoming other before our eyes; what will command attention, for in it will not be one soul but three or four, and they will frighten you for knowing until you turn.

aurora. Is this your Übermensch? Is this for what I'm striving, what I strived for before I knew? Before I read you? Before I imagined...?

conscience. What are you seeking?

aurora. What we become when we ascend and how this earth breaks within me and becomes what I am.

Why would I want to define myself in time when to do so tangles me maddeningly? What did the daemon say? And I see him, mouth beneath erasure, what I invent and blot out, what I annihilate and save. God not wanting to be found. Oh my angel with your dark traction how I watched you sleep, almost kind. My heart slips in darkness, easily finding its way back into ache, oh that horse in the never-ending story, how we find the bottom lest starve.

conscience. Shhh. Put your ear to the alcove: Find the bottomless. Proceed from what you know to be true within you.

Scrolls hidden in a cave surface in the world, for I remember and return. Need draws them out of a past established but a moment ago. And now I've begun to see the others behind my eyes. Is it only the dead ones? Or am I drawing you, too up from the well?

There is truth here, but I have strayed. It has to do with my awareness of a space inside of all-knowing. Am I creating as I go, my awareness of things bringing them into existence? Or is someone directing me from within? His need drawing as well.

Imagination creates. Wisdom exists. One moves and expands while the other is eternal.

conscience. When we left her she'd sprung from the window and now?

aurora. We saved the forest like this and then the swamp. What Human is proving with rats we have always known. Receptivity increases on its way to the world. You are necessary to what I become.

conscience. We had a common mission, yes; it's how we evolved. One saw how it was done, that she could be smarter than what was asked and created a council of like-minded apes to carry along not so much a thought at that point as an impulse to expand. Awareness drew our skulls long, curious time.

aurora. Curiosity. Desire. Seeing and sensing something on the ground before us that promises to be more, a magical key to another world unlocking us, releasing us from the cage of our own limitations, our own limited head, drawing long the skull, naturally expanding.

What do I look like now? Meaning now on the continuum, now at any and no point in time? Light. But light too travels at a speed they say. Nonsense. What is the speed of thought?

How describe, how explain what has not yet come into being without drawing it out, solidifying its form, forming it? How could I stand not to be a god, Nietzsche asks. And so I am God, we are God, our perception expanding the parameters of our world. Adumbration, this that is forming at the margins of my thought, what exists within the pleroma, my awareness bringing it into existence on a material plane. Necessity and I create, for what I see around me in this material world is not what I am, is flawed.

And so I ruminate and dwell, perhaps growing the human brain or catalyzing its evolution, its capacity to apprehend and to reign but not reign, for there is no desire to take away from the beauty and mystery of my world, or to impose my will. I am in awe and in wonder as I sit at the edge of this primordial pond, where to be expands us just as it strains the muscle of the brain.

Let me stay in the child's perspective, everything happening simultaneously now, and yet at the same time sequentially, for this is how a brain orders and makes sense of its world. But that something in the future could indeed affect the past and is constantly affecting the past, for everything is always touching, intersecting, and in growth, that in looking backward or forward there is no longer backward or forward but a matrix, a web of life that expands outward from a point, depending on from which point it is examined. Meaning grows as the mind makes connections, compiles and assembles and grows.

The closer I get to myself the more mystical it all seems, so that at my seams rain, a leaking out when one reaches an epiphanic truth, self in deluge sing! It is this place perhaps where universes meet or where a soul collides with another soul. And what might we accomplish in collaboration, you and I, the voice which speaks without a voice.

Where are the others? For I hear them at times, their laughter grand when they see that I'm coming. Safe, that they are dead and I am the one here on the ground.

17 INSTRUMENT OF BODY

Understand with the instrument of your body why you were made and what you were sent here to do. Within you is the world. Feel the philosopher move through you, having never known. Come, I'll teach you, Nietzsche, my playboy with the bouffant hair. How it has never been about sexes but what we would be inside of each other, things slipping into things, you into me. Who is greater then, I ask you? You in my cave at the top of the hill if you must make yourself larger to fill me? And perhaps that is why the jousting, the pushing out, the fight in you. Come. I have made it like this, and you agreed.

But it is not about these things. Women fill women, men men. Our playing field swept clean. I neither blamed you nor took offence, but laughed as Schopenhauer laughed. When we make it about these things we become limited, small. You struck with lightning. Me here the cave. How tawdry these things become.

conscience. There is no offence to their misunderstanding. How can we recognize what doesn't recognize itself?

18 WE CREATE THE LIGHT IN OURSELVES AND THE DARKNESS

aurora. Are you then the black bird, the thing in me cast off? What would have aberrated and fallen? And with whose voice does it speak but mine?

conscience. The future.

aurora. —

conscience. Go back, and you will see.

aurora. Back where? Into a memory of black pain? Or into one of cloying joy? I don't write this well you know.

conscience. That's judgment again.

aurora. I am judgment. How could I toss this off completely? It has become part of my form, a palimpsest I will never rid myself of.

conscience. Writing on the body of the form dragged. What you will not extract and why would you when this is what you have lived? What we've all lived.

aurora. So the burning woman would have been what?

conscience. All women and her story. History repeats itself, they say. We must be aware of the past not to repeat it. But it is not so. Aware, unaware we go the same ways. This is what happened and then this. To step out would mean seeing something else and moving toward it. But how move toward what doesn't exist?

It starts with what is part of this earth now creating

a space for itself. It is the only way. Listen and live.

aurora. Are you my conscience?

conscience. We have no need for such things. I am. You are. What you have done, Aurora, what you have done.

aurora. What have I done?

conscience. Ahhh. Listen. Geräuscht. Geräte. All white noise filling your head. Get out of the city.

aurora. I am.

conscience. The ones we are killing will be needed for this. The others—we've altered their form—speak too, but they do not know why.

aurora. Why?

conscience. Why we need not heed their warning. It will merely draw us into a path that has happened. You can't live here. You don't. You know it. What speaks dies.

aurora. —

conscience. I am afraid it is too late. Your hair white from bomb. Ash, bomb. Lie down, child. They will take us down.

aurora. You don't mean.

conscience. No, I am not being facetious. Within, where you will see.

Is it but myself who speaks from the surface and says nothing but what fear wills and superfluous nothing? Beat. Beat. Let me live. Take me into a forest that still exists. Affirm. Oh again, this.

conscience. You cannot know what happens.

aurora. But someone needs to lead.

conscience. From where you are. You are already one.

aurora. One what?

conscience. One of those with ears. There is no

need...

aurora. I want to enter your memory then as you enter mine.

conscience. Memory is past. You reside there. It is why you are so far from me. I cannot come to you now.

aurora. You told me to go back. Now why...

conscience. You know why the light has left you. It was as you realized through the angel. We can generate light on our own.

aurora. But I did not do it willfully. It was not my intention.

conscience. Therefore, it is in darkness light.

aurora. What do you mean?

conscience. In the darkness of your thought, in the well, oh the birds and the chisel, in creating the spark. Strike the tool, and there is your power. Let future be. You have done it.

aurora. Let me understand. How?

conscience. Go back. Let us see the room this time. Something took the body down. You were not alone.

aurora. It was May, the suicide month. The room had been painted water lily, so that the light at this hour was green, a vortex to the ceiling. I felt the dark cloth, wings, the cover of darkness, shade, flight in a thing.

conscience. What you felt was the well, darkness dropping, plummeting so hard, a bird forging with the rush, plummeting and rushing past what dark matter, the rushing down the inside, the slinking of kern. All of this creates light, electrical charge, power.

aurora. That we see?

conscience. We create the night in ourselves, the darkness.

aurora. And light? Oh, I'm scared. Shhh. We who?

69

conscience. We. Trust that you know. You've seen things within. Yes, night. Yes, love. The stars burning. Do you want to know how? You love. Burn, and the woman burns. The thoughts you have when no one is looking, what draws their eyes to yours. You will be other. There are things you cannot do yet. But this concept, this cage, breaking out would be storm, and you would know how it felt to transform.

aurora. I would have to leave the world.

conscience. You would have to relinquish what you are.

aurora. Oh to go far from it. I could not return to this body.

conscience. It is why you've come. In detachment is always death.

aurora. I would have to die? But you said we didn't die this time.

conscience. We don't. The coming back wouldn't be necessary if we never left. But severing. There is always this severing. Cutting, punishment, pain for its beauty. Yes, why not? Drop the child. Let her go, and in the blood, power, for the fright it stirs in you has a frequency that lights something. You were conjoined. He, more of the world, but understanding concepts which would bind him to you in ways. He is part of this.

aurora. And I think ghosts, but...

conscience. Yes, brighter forms. How desire might ignite in traverse.

aurora. But would we all...

conscience. Have to let go at the same time? And so the bombs, the fright, and in fright a uniting of heart. The shooting in Connecticut.

aurora. The light of those children.

conscience. What we were told about God was all wrong.

70

There would be unity in spirit is all. It is as with terror, yet the vengeful spirit reaches out and not in and so can do nothing. It is how we give birth to a new world. In the apes' eyes intention and then a voice within with a purpose. All of this is within you. These colliding of parts—nonsense. Do not disregard where you've been. Why would a hero need to fail so miserably? Why would the vehicle of self need a flame? Why would the world heed a prophet when inside it remained unchanged?

aurora. When we found out we weren't animal I would have been part of this force, the impetus.

conscience. Do you know then, what you have done?

aurora. There are things we're not seeing.

conscience. All of this necessary. Do not disregard the flight.

aurora. It's not just me; it's in all of us.

conscience. But it's you. You have seen it. It is why it must be a story. For some to hear a proselytizing one. You know who you are, why you've come. You will need all these things, all that I've told, all you've lived.

aurora. Then who am I? Vessel? Oracle? What is an oracle but nothing of itself?

conscience. You will see what power an oracle has.

aurora. So we will need the ash on the city and the volcano, for the volcano was the one burning inside. But where is the story in all of this? Where is the heroine who threw herself on the ground?

conscience. Where are you?

aurora. —

conscience Where are you?

aurora. I'm in a room of glass.

conscience. A cage?

aurora. A jar whose lid you are removing with the sky.

conscience. Move, Aurora, move!

71

aurora. And I can I can. You are not yet created. We didn't survive.

conscience. Yes, you were tragic. Move on.

aurora. If I sweep my boots out over the cage, if I hold my hair to the light, the winter sky and wind, a sandpaper star scraping its way into light. How we fell in love with music.

conscience. And how long it has been since you sang.

aurora. What we brought with us into the world broken and discarded and let in a trailer park and in a suitcase in a barn cluttered with rats.

conscience. Nonsense. Nonsense. What do you want?

aurora. To be what saves, to take us out of this night. I want it to be like it was.

conscience. How was it, child?

aurora. When the wind spoke and the prophet took heed, only this time I am the prophet and the wind and what takes heed.

conscience. Yes.

aurora. But they will say it cannot be, and I will doubt myself.

conscience. Who will say it? Try. Fail. Dasein. It is what it means.

aurora. Will I have to do it again? To collect what of me.

conscience. That would be tragic. Remember what it was to be the storm.

aurora. But one can't remain at this level and here at once.

conscience. And why not? You did for years, until you dropped the orb into the sand and let it be buried. You've not lived anymore since then.

aurora. Because I've been trampled, because I haven't felt any more than this page and what it is to be a woman getting old.

conscience. There will always be things dragging you under in world, but your eyes, what you see. Stay down. See the past in your future. Shatter it. Be the animal, the monkey-ape. Do you remember the story? What you said about your dad? This all has a place here.

aurora. My dad?

conscience. At the Peabody Museum: Evolution of Man. *You mean this is what Daddy used to look like?* And you felt so ashamed when they laughed at you. Yet it's brilliant! All of it right for your cause. If we can conflate time, we can get this done. It is not always about the path. Do not dismiss the things in you that want to achieve what you know comes. There is a turning point. (Oh, how every poet gasps when they learn it's all agrarian, verse, the turn in the line. We're tied to the land. Watch how the line ends, and the tractor heads down...*Landscape with the Fall of Icarus.* It all depends upon a red wheelbarrow...) Do not disregard what indelible stroke you carry.

aurora. But I am detached. I don't feel. I haven't since, oh Anne Carson, what you've done pairing cats with the mundane. What has kept us so long turning? How many flicks of the page before something sparks, catches fire, and burns us into the ash drifting out over fishing boats, me, the cow fished out of the bay.

conscience. Oh, Aurora, it's a trope. You need it. Need it all. Now write!

19 THE END

There were stories. Meat Cove, how you got your name. Once told, they are the body's, an instrument, threaded box kept from wind, swan wings scattered over fields, waste, takes or discards. So many things become one, a multiplicity of self, how I can be earth can be God. How a girl might be volcanic, a temper of fright. How cattle might be thrown from a crag. How meat from the shipping boats passing the headland might drift and drift into a cove. How I might be falling in the form of a bird, how that bird might rise and be found. How in the tide I might be dragged and how dragging would sound, how resilient the heart in this light. There will be a leitmotiv: metal in wind, a silo, a girl. Music will sustain this, the body-lute dragged and not dragged. What did I hear once that pacified me? God is in her kingdom, and everything is right in the world. Right.

aurora. I was a girl once. This does not have to be painful. This does not have to hurt.

Oh my God, you were there!

conscience. Yes, Aurora. Write. Tell me what you saw.

aurora. The nightmares of snakes. How a girl might be dragged. How awful it'd be for the man.

conscience. He wouldn't know what to do with you, bag of pain, but to push you along on the path. How little has changed, you abrading yourself, ugly, ugly, ugly girl, ass to the shadows so he would not see your dimpled thighs. If you'd only known the perfect beauty you still are. Yes, you with the downy skin, fur covering you like a pelt. You with your animal kept up within, with the fight that leaks out of your mouth. And the dark gouge beneath your eye. Love the animal. Love as you love broken, love as a bruise, the jagged beauty of self as a scar. You will never be the same beauty as you are with a forearm that aches still. And will you be ashamed that your cuts aren't as deep as the suicide's? The numbness, dead sensation, concentration of nerves. I know flooding, undulation, a dark heady guilt, a murderess killing itself.

aurora. Why?

conscience. Because she could not live anymore. Because you would not let her fly off but over the cove in a poem. Because an archon had come in the guise of love with his vice grip and chained her heart to a rock. And her heart bled into it until such beauty as runs down the back of the earth.

aurora. Now I know you.

conscience. Yes. I watched you bleed yourself and slipped down the walls deep within where nothing could get to us.

aurora. Us. We are the same.

conscience. In part. Will you know my story yet?

aurora. Who then was the one with the slingshot?

conscience. It was you, killing what she could no longer control. Killing you for holding her there against the stone, for saying wait, love, he will... Wait, he will love. (There. She surfaces, the black mag.) For somehow he'd become the world to you, and if he couldn't love us we were doomed. Wait love. Now do you get it? Hold still.

This is what it is to love you, you wrote. *This fire /*

in the wind, the stillness / of the sky, a borrowed tent where you held me...

Hold still until you become the rapist. Hold still until we're stilling his hands.

aurora. And the heart, this purple lub.

conscience. That is the liver that you have there. Here's the heart.

aurora. How would I know what it was like to feel its weight in my hand, to smell the sticky metal of its blood?

conscience. You'd been bled so many times, Love.

aurora. But the heart. How would I know the heart?

conscience. You didn't. See above. You didn't belong to him.

aurora. Metal: the leitmotiv. What was it? Dogs in tin and the expansion ticking like a metronome, metering the crescent moon across the sky. The girl on the floor of a house expanding in ice. Thawing would illicit metal, thawing like sheets of pounded glass. How would this advance us?

conscience. It's part of consciousness. Seeing what you'd done from the perspective of parts. How beautifully complex one can be.

aurora. And now?

conscience. And now we live.

aurora. Would Human have to die?

conscience. You killed it. Go on. Tell me what happens in the writing when you circle around and around?

aurora. It is the hawk refining its flight pattern, circling the terrain. The cat chasing its tail, mirroring my inner world: I've been going in circles trying to figure an end to a cycle that has no end. The only way out is to break the routine. Around and around brings nothing without the will to seek beyond.

conscience. History repeats itself is a mantra keeping us stuck. Get to the tree. Concentric movement. The circle expands. Infinity another cyclical figure. A snake swallowing its tail. Let it eat itself then into oblivion that we might start anew. Lion, child. Thumb, forefinger, middle, ring, pinky, pinky, ring,... Until you figure out what takes you beyond is merely the will to move beyond what we've done.

aurora. —

conscience. You are the light from the realm of the self that goes on. Conflate time. Collapse it in your mind. There is no precedent for this. Something in you will know, I trust. How we can extend into the world and will a transformation. How we can extend so deep within ourselves that we'd ignite. Go down go down.

BOOK 3

COME FROM INVISIBLE THINGS TO THE END OF THOSE
THAT ARE VISIBLE, AND THE VERY EMANATION OF
THOUGHT WILL REVEAL TO YOU HOW FAITH IN THOSE
THINGS THAT ARE NOT VISIBLE WAS FOUND IN THOSE
THAT ARE VISIBLE, THOSE THAT BELONG TO
UNBEGOTTEN FATHER.

THE SOPHIA OF JESUS CHRIST

The mind slips between the vast grey nothingness of a decimated planet and the sterility of a hospital room as consciousness apperceives one and then the other, attempting to apprehend revelations that advance it beyond its capacity. The eternal form surfaces in the form of a woman robed in red, everything moving toward the apocalyptic end, the image of red birds no longer contained in a book but on an internal plane.

What you have done. Aurora finds herself gradually detaching from the secular world, relinquishing those things that belong to a world of forms, a world of erred thinking, strayed from God and breaching the light realm through the web of illusion. Here at the culmination are Nietzsche's 7 devils, Buddhism,'s 7 chakra's, Plotinius' 7 stages of wisdom , Jacob's ladder, Ezekiel's seals, Mohammed's night journey through the 7 gates, and here the 7 attributes of the planetary governors, the 7 attributes of the phenomenal world, beyond which is Reality.

1 MOON. LUNACY. FLUX.

It was not a place but consciousness. Once we arrived, worlds would fall, and there in the distance the wires...

conscience. Shhh. If you freak out about it, it will grow.
aurora. I've had enough. I can't.

"What happened to her head?" *It's Manley.*
"She claims she was removing dross." *A voice I do not recognize.* "Ask her. It's rather droll."
"Aurora?"
—

"Wipe some of that blood from her eyes so I can see where she's focusing."
"She's not focusing. Her eyes seem to be in epileptic fit. Oh, there we go. Aurora?"

aurora. You've shut my mouth down. Why?
conscience. Look, we can still do this.
aurora. I can't. Please. I feel like I've been split open. Look, I have seams at the sides of my neck. Look! Seams! Seams!

"What is she doing?"
"Get Harry in here. Go for god's sake! Cindy, the eyes."

aurora. Why is it the most difficult thing to remember that you were benign? The pressure was mine. You were saying something else. When I finally wouldn't answer, you put me to sleep.

Ω

She is in the cave, which is to say that I am in the cave. Sybil. In the silence, I can remember machine, and remembrance brings silence. I am in love here with the way the world fills with light. I have a secret, and that secret belongs to a cave, and in that cave is...

I am in the cave, and I am a red bird darting at the walls, for inside my chest are birds in flight in a sky as big as the world inside. And I know myself as life. And I know myself. And I am singing! And tears are streaming down my face. A warbling voice sets out and touches the trees and casts its light about, and it is about all this teeming, all this life.

Ω

There is blood on the face of the patient as she regains consciousness and springs upright, blood streaming from her eyes affright.

conscience. Stay down. Stay down inside. The world wasn't yours; then it was in a flash. I was with you. It is me on the table. Flip the coin. Possibility shattered. It was just a dream. A nightmare of possible possibilities. Shhhh, child. Hush. The blood is life. *She is wiping it from my cheeks, brushing it into my hair which has whitened and yellowed from bomb.*

Go down. Go down where the birds crack life open in

a crossroads of branch, a divining rod. Draw it over the sand. See that you can, that here you can do anything; you will it to be. On the island is a species which has evolved its hands that it might crack open carbuncles on volcanic rock.

aurora. Whether or not the spider was a demiurge. Whether or not something had to be broken and destroyed...

On our island, I am a bird whose eyes say responsible, whose spirit says now, whose soul is a black metal box I wear in my chest, its doors flung wide, its vacant expanse ever a hole in me, ever streaming, raw, vacant, nothing but hollow. That a soul might not be able to stand or carry itself but for awareness of the alchemical nature in all things raw. What for its darkness might emanate light, what in falling might catch fire, what in burning might ascend.

conscience. We are the spider, the alchemical rendering of the world in a star.

aurora. And of the red birds in my chest, the birds and the woman in red brocade who I am when you ask me who I am. And I will say to you as the girl approaches, I will say to you come, for this is what you were made for; this is why you have come. And today, I will say three words to you. Today, I will add four more, and you will begin to transform, and our earth will begin to form, for we are not to notice its passing but its beauty in our strength and its communion in our lives so very necessary.

Do you remember? she is saying of the power lines flagging the land. And there is a remnant, which we will watch from season to season as the earth forgets its presence, and it simply disappears.

85

Ω

There is a face weeping at the base of a mountain. It is fallen.

"Why would you have shown her that?"

"She wanted to know it." They are speaking about me, the clinicians, the one with the red-haired hand. Who are they to put me here? But in asking I know they have not. They are simply rooms from here in my mind where I have put something into motion.

"Give this to her."

The ribbon that was decumbent on the floor is in his hand. He is opening my hand, laying it across my palm, and closing my fingers over the fabric. It is sun-bleached orange, weathered, and frayed. How blood would dry in the heart. How deep the coil unfurl.

Then they are gone, and I am here on a gurney in a room that keeps opening out until all is rubble, all white debris. And I remember her hand and wish I could feel it now on the ash. The sky is two charcoal gray sails saturated and lowered on a blanket of fog.

"Come back down to earth with me," my husband says, but there's something I must do I have done.

2 MERCURY. FALSE THINKING.

conscience. Get up and get to the tree.

aurora. But you told me to go toward something was to see it first within me.

conscience. What do you want?

aurora. To listen to the elements, to be alone with them.

conscience. Continue to hold your heart out.

aurora. I've become so detached from my surroundings that I don't recognize myself as part of the world. I don't want back in and that scares me.

conscience. You are outside. Why would you want back in?

aurora. Because there is no precedent for this.

conscience. What you have done.

aurora. What do you want from me? I have nothing.

Ω

conscience. What do you need that you think that you lack?

aurora. To recognize something like myself and be recognized.

conscience. You want to save what thrives in being, what is beautifully and naturally alive. What if the point were just to explore? Would that be enough? To choose from the forms only perpetuates a system of denigration and lack. Who are you when you enter the deepest center of your being? Who you are, you must bring to the world.

aurora. Instead of carrying it out... Instead of carrying it out like I did. Anima mundi, the feminine divine. When I saw how a soul could be trampled and raped, I took mine out of the world. It is the same with the transport of earth soul, to think that I could take her out that she might not see and be affected by what is being done to her. It is me, isn't it? I'm extracting the feminine from the world stage. I think I'm getting it now.

conscience. How sweet that you were trying to protect her as you tried to protect yourself. This is what kills us remember?

aurora. I don't want to remember anymore. Defunct, all of the things that I love.

conscience. Hold your heart out bravely. There you are. Turn your eyes toward the sky and the creatures. They support you.

aurora. But we are killing them.

conscience. You are not, Aurora. It is why. An alchemist will be needed to turn the world to light. We are not to save the planet. Our efforts would be in vain. Leave it to the ruling men to finish off as they will. It will not be long. Our work is to meet the darkness within us, to integrate it, to expand. To discover ourselves into being, body as emanation of a being that would grow. Let go of external measurement. Let go of power and greed. Let go of money as motivation; it only kills things. Seething, scythe in the heart chakra.

The transformation comes in not being able to put back the gift of sight, knowledge forward and backward, vision and insight, the feeling one is so much a part of the world's consciousness as to be conscious of the world.

3 VENUS. GRACE OF FORM NOT REALITY.

I am the priestess in the cave at the top of the mountain waving the red flag of her gown.

You are keeping me from the pain of this, keeping it from touching my heart, keeping it out of the metal box, yet I feel it in these birds dying. Oh world, my love, I cannot touch you to my heart anymore. What I have done is nothing. What I have done is to sit in the wings and wait for someone to call me out, wait for someone to say we need the oracle, the priestess in red...

Now I am not being asked to save this thing. It dies. It has died in my heart, and maybe that is what I feel now, for I do not know whether to be happy that light lives in me or to feel the albatross die and know that I am a part of its death that I am a part of a world that destroys. And so I die, albatross. I die for I cannot stop this thing we have set in motion, for with my heart I have seen I cannot save, just watch as creatures reach me in the daylight that were nocturnal once.

Ω

In the forest, a trinity of rat snakes falls at my feet, and the black earth turns fluid around the gray stones where I stand in movement dead, holding my white heart in place. They are a sign of wisdom, an alert to the creature rising within, a reason for the palsy, the head swells and light.

I sleep in the forest. I wake on a rattler that slips up my arm and unfurls in my skull. I feel its expansion: my face tremoring over the coming days, vertigo on standing. I am the snake at the snake's command, this that will not feed on flesh but berries. I have no desire but its unfurling, the ecstatic pulse of electrified joy, a synaptic firing within.

I proceed peripatetic, drawing beauty into me from the surround, feeling myself light, buoyant, that I might enter a vulture in flight through the valley, that I might feel the pulse of earth, sense energy expand and hold me in the sky. That the earth be my earth. The bird, bird I made. That all might be inside me and without. That I wouldn't want to escape this reality but be forever in communion with what I had made. That there would be a time to leave, this thing within me coming through me into world, that space would not be vacant but consummate light.

Ω

The meditations have become physical. Whatever it is that is in me that commands without a voice compels my arms to be lifted palms up at my sides, so that I picture myself the goddess Durga with a crown on my head and three sets of arms. Sudden energy pronates the right hands, and I remain poised, questioning this thing that moves through me though unwilling to oppose it or put my arms down. As if generated by my hands' position, its energy passes elliptically hand to hand enclosing me within an egg of joy. Synaptic pulses surge and tear through my head then tremor in my jaw. My torso sways then circles clockwise over the floor. Wider in concentric movement, it glides into a figure eight tipped on its side, infinite enumeration.

A white square emerges from the darkness. I concentrate as it sharpens in form, when I feel a tug at the base of my eyeballs as of something being pulled into rotation. What feels an orb in my skull begins to spin vertically, tipping me forward, my eyeballs jerking in resistance and my head vibrating from the speed until I am slipping, the egg still circulating through my hands, the orb still revolving, everything in movement. Then the image before me becomes inverted, a black square on the surface of light, and I catch myself on the chair and emerge.

What are we? What is body when it can be taken like this and entered by some other force?

4 SUN. AMBITION.

I have understood that it is about letting go of something that once gone won't be remembered until it perhaps returns to us. We cannot concern ourselves, however, with whether or not it will return but only the letting go, and the letting go is the release of ego I suspect, the release of a claim to fame. The girl who thought she was... The girl who thought it was her task to awaken the world, to save it, to change it, alone that she might say I did this. All of this I'm afraid must be released, everything but the desire to see the light return to the world, that spot of grass, a hole in the night sky, inversion. But even this. Oh how duality sings! Duality within the monistic world. Oh love! Oh hate oh grace oh light oh world!

And again the desire not to be sage but vessel, the oracle from which the divine reaches the world, the conveyance only, but not the message; this was too much. This I relinquish. It is yours. Take it! I want to sing! To sing! To sing! But not to carry the burden of writing the song that takes the world from darkness again.
conscience. Hush.

Ω

In the mirror, I spy a green fleck in the corner of my eye. I press my face to the glass in scrutiny when a translucent haw appears, and the lid flickers shut. I blink and sinewy green weeds slip across my eyeballs then settle at the center in piles. There's a perverted tickle in my cheekbone as I pick at an edge with my fingernails, and the blade licks past the flesh on the underside, tugged from the socket where it lay flat and snug. My eyes then grow the size of my hands, and the vegetation propagates until I am wresting the blades free by the fistful, tirelessly and blind.

Thereafter, the air glimmers, no remnants in hand or eye. There will be visions strangely colored in the coming days: the sun the center of a rainbow, the sky liquid light and tincture red.

aurora. If we are one and some have evolved, what happens to the rest of us? Is this why I am alone at the end?

conscience. You have always been alone. You preferred it like this.

5 MARS. CONFLICT.

When I finally comprehend, it is in the car with Manley, and I no longer know what is story and what is my life.

conscience. Only the earth dies.
aurora. Only the earth?
conscience. And Human. Do you remember?
aurora. Please, let us change this. It was my charge.

The ash. We die here. Ashes, ashes, we all fall down and in falling rise. Glints of ember coming off a flame. A column, a flume, something escaping into the dark. There is something I must remember. What is then at the bottom of the straw? *Straw?*

I want to run I want to run I want to run from this.

"Come back down to earth with me," Manley says again, yet I am so deep within as to have emerged on the other side.

aurora. You have to take me out. I can't. I will not make it.
conscience. We have never known her. Do you get it now? Anima mundi, the feminine divine, because you kept yourself hidden; parts you felt too precious to see. He is stepping on them now.
aurora. I asked for this. I know. Have you made it pos-

sible for me any other way?

But I know that answer. I know. He is chastising me. He doesn't want to give credence to thoughts of things he can't see or feel.

conscience. Turn around.

I am not here anymore. I am not here. I am not here in the car with Manley...

"Sell your book," he says.

aurora. I have no interest in commerce. So little makes sense in this world. Maybe we are meant to destroy. So a patriarchy dies. But with it go my animals, my trees, my hide. Where is the meaning in this?

conscience. What you have done what you have done what you have done.

aurora. I am dying. I thought it was symbolic.

conscience. Show him.

aurora. If I could get her to the surface, beyond the one he knows. If I could just let him in on all I know. Microcosm, macrocosm: if in my own life I could be fully present, asserting who I am...

conscience. Not this way.

aurora. So I was right to protect her? The coffer vacant and yet filled. So little of this matters, if you can understand or not. If you can, this is for you. I will not waste my time with what cannot. This is not meant to save. I think I am getting that now. But what do I do with it? What do I do?

conscience. Be. Carry the world soul. We will end. See it as now you are aware: death as life; life death. It is Ego that wants to save. I destroy and make alive. There is no time, but expansion.

Ω

aurora. If we die, what is the sense in all of this?

conscience. Eternal recurrence.

aurora. Eternal recurrence. Body container. Stuck in a form. Is this what Nietzsche came to, what I did not understand him accepting, the swallowed head? Uroboros. Having gone back and yet being for the first time at this level of awareness. For what speaks knows all; operates from a higher plane. Therefore it is not this loop, this cycle. [But how could it not be?] We are blown from it destroyed. [And yet still here.] Transmuted from form, released like a god. Am I not taken deeper and deeper away from this world?

conscience. And into it at once. The body is not arbitrary. It is why eating in a soul.

aurora. What will we be? A question expands us. We *are* in it. Yet I cannot know until I expand.

Words are the vehicle to enter into body, where they catch fire, revelation, change. I can open the heart chakra. I can hold open the cage. And so I am evolving: this, what racks the body's cage, what sends tremors through the skull and quivers in the jaw, what makes me other inside.

6 JUPITER. JUDGMENT.

There are some among us who can see into shadows; some who have reached the teacher at the heart of the world. There are some who thought this was a story; some with light so pure as to absorb darkness and go out.

I am a keeper of the light. Maybe this is how it was entrusted. Maybe our unveiling wasn't yet but now. For in remaining out of the world, in remaining in the cave, saying I don't have a place in this, I have allowed this condition to go on. I have allowed the world to be trampled. I have allowed the patriarchy to reign and to define what is worth in the world when I know another world.

conscience. Tell me of that world.
aurora. What if I must die in this one?
conscience. You have died. Dying is a form of letting go. It is not as you imagine. When you dwell in the darkness, it consumes. Bring the story to light. Bring the story, the story of the world in you. How firm the box. How raw and damaged like the bovine stomach, like the intestines of the pig whose snout they've snapped off for their folly. Turn the light to the darkness. Turn around. When the light of a star is so bright that it consumes itself, you are that star. We need your light. Microcosm.

Be the story, that beautiful light that poured through you in the past. It knew what would come as it knew your attention on the darkness spawned the darkness. You know another way. You can heal the tears in the esophagus and in the lining of the organs of bears.

aurora. Oh that pain is so raw in me. So ragged and despairing.

conscience. But not flat, not dead. It is pain that lives, pain that if you'd get closer is lit with love. And that is where the light comes in. Come, although you almost cannot bear it. Although you could not stand up on the physical plane in this moment if you tried, that ache in you is life; this, the alchemical work of the soul where you've the power in the simple act of consciousness to turn common metal into gold. And so yes, listen to the cry of the earth as some say we must. Let it weep through a body that too has been ravaged, geminating your pain as you had imagined when you laid down your wings at the boy's side, when their whiteness drew his pain to the surface, so that white was his frailty displayed, a bone beak chipped in remembrance; the body's water a pool, an imprint, a staved rod of beget.

aurora. Something has happened to clear the world's den. Something has drowned the wolf in the lamp. The heart hiccups in pain; in paroxysm breath leaves me holed. Vacancy vacancy touch me red. In the going down it is lit, incinerated. Oh to exist here. How explain the black expanse behind my breast. I forgot how to do this. I forgot.

conscience. Just look at it. Look. Step back from the shadow and see that the webs were your light, the spider your light, cast from your form into world, and that this was alchemy. This is all I am asking from you, to see what you've done. What you marvel at, what now draws tears from your enlightened eyes is love brought to the world. Just as the songs the prayer ones are singing are bringing love and so healing. This love exists and is just as valid in existence. Continue to feel and to transform. Feel and to transform. Go down go down this is life. The songs we are singing when we enter this night will light the world with love.

aurora. I am almost happy, but the joy this time is fleeting.

conscience. Others will catch on; you will feel them. You have given them an invitation in the web. Your light is strong. They see it. Tend the light. Stoke it. You remarkable shadow thrower. There is hope.

aurora. Do we still die here?
conscience. The world dies.

7 SATURN. GRAVITY. DEATH. THE PERMANENCE OF THE ILLUSIONARY STATE.

I am not being asked to save anything. There is a knowing that asks only to be known. Conscious, we evolve. There is no urgency or agenda. There is no outer process or set of feats to achieve. There is only this. Be more aware and in awakening what is beyond rises from sleep. Again potential. Am I to hope? I can no longer hope. It is done. There is beginning. A release of souls in the light. This light, fire, a bomb, white shriek. Sparks. Flames ascending, the black soot smoke that is their child that is chiding coming down to the earth coming down. What can be sad? Ouroboros. Again that star that has concealed its light.

I am at peace in the stillness. There is nothing to be done. How liberating this one realization, that one doesn't have to do to be. I am. Be. Be still. My heart leaps onto my heart in embrace.

When the light leaves the world, it will only be a hole, shining.

THE END OF NATURE

Aurora tries to wake the internal bird and nearly kills herself in grief, a destitute darkness having taken inhabitance within her chest, a darkness so heavy she cannot rise from the ground without pittance (grace) from God, or an angel, for one shoots arrows of light into the wings of the bird. Her surrender takes her into the consciousness of God. She walks in light, her body no longer her own.

Aurora is trying to make sense through human mind when what is transpiring on the spiritual level has opened her to another consciousness, what is cosmic or God. She will die and die again until what no longer serves her is left to ash, until she can relinquish the sensory realm for the eternal, or real.

1 THE SPIRIT WHOSE BODY IS EARTH

Some say the inner worlds are darkening, that what our earth has sustained reflects a 'darkening of the light'. That it is not only the physical world that we are annihilating but the sacred underworld of spirits as well. That the earth has a soul, her appellation, Anima Mundi.

To carry the light means to carry the darkness. Hence I go down until I am a bird lying beside a bird, being swept back and forth in the waves. I want to be nearer to this creature, to enfold within my body its pain, but in wanting find I am the earth dead and heavy, turned on its side. I cry out, nothing separating me from its fate or lifeless form.

There is something in my throat chakra making it hard to breathe, something prying open the box, creeping into my heart, something of gravity in the murky light that causes me to survey the prodigious wings extending my arms, the hands becoming fulcrum of elbow joint, great plumes yellow-dead in the loam. What more I am I cannot see. If I have legs, they are inutile. I try to move the body, try again to conjure the light. I've transformed pain this way before. My breast flashes gold then dies away. If I could fly I say, appealing to God, but I can't. I can't.

Fulgid arrows drop from a lucent cloud overhead and radiate across the wings. So I am to be a phoenix I think.

They will burn and I will fly. They do not burn, however, and I cannot fly.

I can only lie there and know none come.

2 A BROKEN PROMISE

conscience. To watch you go to the bird in darkness, you golden like flame, casting an aureole on the bird, laying yourself down inside that through its body golden light might radiate. Stillness. Just a flame flickering, drawing in, expanding, and a creature heaving a sigh. I know less and less what God is but all. For here it is in attempt to lift a wing, you set it down. Death long deplete. One feels a broken promise. A heart stolen from its cage. What has taken this bird from the sky is love, profligate. Light gone. It happened when the children were stolen, cut from the night was he. And down he sank into your body where you'll find him again and again. His will be the void, the cold metal.

In the beyond, it is done. Here is the body the daemon dragged. Your consciousness has grieved her.

aurora. Then the bird is the world?
conscience. Part of her consciousness. She didn't know the extent of her wounds. She didn't know the feral nature of greed until you wore her body. On the floor, when you could not breathe, she could not breathe, for it is again in touching down all you brought with you she saw.
aurora. —
conscience. What are you seeing?
aurora. I will be sick. This I cannot again. Jyoti Singh. I

carry her. Oh, what has loved us deplete. Again I cry out, yet nothing comes but this being who can't use its wings.

conscience. Who are you?

aurora. Vala.

conscience. A place.

3 THE GRIEF GOD

Anima had had enough. The Grief God had her anesthe-tized in the wings that she might not be privy to what we had done to her.

Yet I brought it into her consciousness: the way that girl's light went out, the way they took the soul. There is darkness so black that it does this, this under-human that has come. We had thought that this was a story, but for the selling of the soul they have come. Oh, heart box aching, for how can a metal box not hurt against the flesh of a human breast? And still she will not let me near this pain though like that bird I push my heart to the thorn, for to be empty like this is love.

conscience. You are to move her to a place where she can breathe again and attempt to heal. You will need to take her out.

aurora. If I were to return with the will to move that bird, would its form exist? Could I locate it again? Oh, if grief could do this! My body is full of stones. My arms, my hands, my womb, stone. Energy draws from the walls of my skin, I am worn, pulled taut from the nerves. Strung. To think, no one would ever know what we had done to put us back on course.

conscience. What course? Are you still trying to save? You will have to let that go to do anything here.

aurora. Let it go? How can I when my neglect has

caused her suffering? Snake in the depths, will you allow that something has changed in me?

conscience. These are not our ways, *she warns.*

aurora. I cannot make sense of this. I cannot let this world die and not die, for it is me that you are killing. You let me destroy myself as you look on. You, who can do anything. And now? Should I look on? Why move my heart in this way, and then tell me to let go? I don't know what to do or how to live in this world.

conscience. This world cannot be saved, and you wouldn't want to save it.

aurora. But the earth. What happens to those that have been so abused?

conscience. It is as yourself.

aurora. Did the earth need to know darkness for what she was to become?

conscience. In the darkness she has become.

Ω

What am I: a chest held open, faded thread, a man on an island wishing us dead? Madness. These birds: children of war and banishment, thought banished from the brains of men. Under-human was here. I watched how you destroyed, for to put myself in your path, you'd have ravished me under your thresher, your gun, your manmade madness and war. Beauty rise. I cannot live, knowing.

4 DRAGGING OFF THE CARCASS FOR THE DEVAS CANNOT FLY

If one were to wake in her dying body to carry her from here that she not witness what we'd done. She would need an alchemist to save her, to open her to her light and to ascend with her to ascend.

Quite dead the devas and wood elves, quite dead the woodland sprite, what we have around us a dying star that has given her power and light. My chest bleeds. I feel a tiny aperture below my right breast where a trickle of blood leaks out. I will go to the bird on the ground, angel or deva, anima, divine, alone that she sees my light.
    Oh that it were so easy!

Ω

aurora. So it is I have found you at the bottom of the world, bird, entered your spirit, vacant, and breathed that you might feel again the darkness of the earth soul fallen, the face at the bottom of the mountain.
    conscience. Breathe, and ember lit with flame will grow. Breathe gold, keep breathing, stay. Stay with this creature in the dark.
    aurora. Oh to sing I would need to awaken the heart and to feel this creature's pain. Is this what it means to

dissolve the ego? To want only to give to something dead, that it become lit, that I become nothing, unborn? You will have to trick me here, for one does not go willingly to a place of tremendous pain. She is led around and through, subversively until she is forever breaking open on this place and in breaking healing this thing. No will could prepare one to step into such flames of slow burning.

Is this what it means to end?

conscience. You cannot be afraid of not coming back.

aurora. It would take a snake lifting its head.

conscience. Get to the tree.

aurora. Shall I enter that bird I might die.

5 WITH THE LIGHT OF A BURNT OUT STAR

aurora. We are the star burnt out, shadows in shade. Balloons at the pool bob like people in recurrent movement, dead. And I am afraid to go down there knowing this not as story but a place with creatures I have no right to disturb, creatures whose exile and demise we claimed as our right.

conscience. You do not have to take ownership of this, Aurora. It isn't yours but the men.

aurora. I was alive and did nothing. I was alive.

conscience. When the words catch fire, the creature will see your light.

aurora. What if she didn't know until I'd awoken in her? What if she was safe in her ignorance?

conscience. Consciousness.

aurora. To ask this bird to rise, to blow on its heart, to know the current that runs through us could jolt this thing alive. Yet I have no right to wake this spirit. How can I be here? How can I touch the spaces that are raw in it knowing sadness killed the bird?

conscience. Lie with it a moment. Know the birds that came to accompany you down; know light on rising.

aurora. I kiss its feathered head, but the heart won't open to die again. Therefore, there is nothing to be done, nothing to ask of a spirit that's given all.

conscience. But Aurora, you know the dark places, not

colorless but erased, a strand without light, a ghost strand.

aurora. But I am the moon. Can I be the moon reflecting the light of God?

conscience. How many times you would die in the poems I did not know.

A corona moves over the orb as if something cast on it an aureole.

Ω

The earth did not know it was dying, for the Grief God had taken it under the world. It could not bear what was being done to it...

aurora. Shall we wake the creature?
conscience. Let it see your light.

In its pure beauty it could not bear how it is children are gunned down in a classroom. Oh, if you could see the light rise. They had come to let you see. They had given themselves to this task. And Jyoti Singh. Let her not see what has been done; let us not see, for to see... And so the Grief God has her, and the devas all have fallen. But the one who has taken me out of this world and forbidden my entrance again. I will follow her to the center, let her light become my light.

Ω

I have to believe we have her. The rest is a dying star, an imprint of memory. We have her wounded soul, we, the keepers of the light. It is as they have said: an alchemist will be needed to ignite the world's light; like a star burnt out we walk on. This will be a terrible moment. How to awaken a creature we've all but destroyed.

conscience. Do not be afraid of what you will do you have done. Step through the door you have made in the sky.
aurora. If the earth is a soul. I am. You are.

Ω

You have been down there. It is enough, something tells me. It is not Conscience, however, but what surrounds and witnesses. Watchers. Twice they have visited in the night, for I have felt their presence close to human, but a purple shade impalpable. So it is, we have moved the earth soul to a plane adjacent to the plane of light.

She will rise into the darkness, crawl until she can see, until she can make out shadows in the light and then move us beyond this cave. I will stay with her. I will no longer have a function on earth. Their battle will go on without us. Their avarice and greed. I am alone in the darkness holding a stave of light from which the new will be born.

aurora. The watchers are ready. Will the earth be again?
conscious. Her soul must recover.

Oh, how I bleed. I will go outside and warm my heart.

Ω

I am the instrument and the one playing and the

AFTERWORD

It was not about saving but redemption; seeing that I could not die here, that love would be enough to kindle a light. Therefore, there is no fear, just sadness, for destroying and defaming what was sacred and divine, so that it wouldn't be as I thought. For how can one not live out the sadness? How dare I create something new when we had not yet learned, when the destruction of the kingdoms goes on? But this is judgment, something of a world I release.

It is why you are alone at the end, Aurora of the dawn. We go on.

Ω

I saw a field which had been cultivated for sod, a field lay waste, cleared of its green rug. Although what had been vegetal and verdant was no longer, its absence was present and so its presence, more profound. In gnosis, I felt the removal of and disregard for what I can only term anima mundi. She in me offended, it touched the wound. It lit the wound up, and again there was that nonduality in the light that ascends flame and dies, for something died in me in that moment. Something stabbed and penetrated the well.

It wasn't representative, but the apperception of life being disregarded and used which brought with it a penetrating and divine sense of pain, so that I gasped for my psyche gaped with wound. Again vacancy. Again instantaneous knowing, consciousness of another form. Awareness at another level. And I think it is this awareness that inspires love, for I am exploding with love for this process, for this awareness. I don't know. Something has changed in me. In my heart what was dark and vacant is liquid gold and yet so black as to be empty and metal, hollow, a box.

Thus, in a field absent of vegetation what is missing informs its light. Oh how can one explain such things? They must be experienced, felt. It is this for which my spirit leaps inside and wants to live, wants to make our place in the world of things!

Ω

With the abuser, I simply stopped wanting to abuse myself, and he transformed. I learned to recognize his hands as my own; I learned to look within and to love myself. How can I apply the same concept in the world?

Then comes the voice. Recognize it. Recognize your divine and feminine right to inhabit the world. Recognize your own intelligence, wisdom, and humanity and know that they are sacred. Shine. You are not alone. Your physical world is an extension of your being, a reflection of the lover in love.

Ask the divine for wisdom, and she will come to you. Ask her for a sign of her presence; it will be. Ask her to design a pathway. Do not compromise yourself. Ever. Do not laugh when you are afraid. Do not take his words into your mouth when you don't feel them. Do not be afraid.

This is where we begin. But first we must end. Die to yourself. Be reborn. Go into the darkness. It is there you

NOTES AND ACKNOWLEDGEMENTS

A version of "Asylum" was published in *Garbanzo Literary Journal,* Volume 4.

"The End" references a number of images as they appear in *The Terrifying Angel.*

Book 3 chapter titles find their roots in "On the Nature of the Godhead," a lecture by Manly Palmer Hall.

"The End of Nature" begins with a reference to Llewellyn Vaughan Lee's *Darkening of the Light*, a poignant exploration of the human inclination to destroy.